Disney's

The HUNCHBACK OF NOTRE DAME

Ladybird

High above the city of Paris, in the bell tower of the great cathedral of Notre Dame, lived a shy and lonely young man called Quasimodo.

Quasimodo's master was the evil Judge Frollo, who hated all gypsies. He had been responsible for the death of a young gypsy woman twenty years earlier. As punishment, the Archdeacon had ordered him to look after the woman's tiny baby – Quasimodo.

Since then, Frollo had kept Quasimodo hidden in the cathedral, telling him he was a monster – too ugly to go outside. Now it was Quasimodo's job to ring the cathedral's bells each day so all the city could hear.

Today was a special day in Paris. It was the Festival of Fools, the biggest festival of the year, where everything was topsy turvy! Everyone was enjoying the fun of the day.

In a street near the cathedral, a beautiful gypsy girl called Esmeralda played her tambourine while her pet goat, Djali, danced. A crowd had gathered to watch them.

Also watching was a young soldier called Phoebus, Frollo's new Captain of the Guard. As he watched Esmeralda, their eyes met, and for a moment they gazed at one another. Suddenly, another gypsy signalled that there was danger nearby and Esmeralda and Djali fled down an alley to hide.

Phoebus made his way to the Palace of Justice and reported to Frollo. From a balcony above the town square, they watched the festival.

"Look – gypsies," said Frollo, angrily. "I believe they have a safe haven within the walls of this very city. It's called the Court of Miracles."

"And what are we to do about that, Sir?" asked Phoebus.

In reply, Frollo viciously crushed an ants' nest he had found on the balcony wall. Phoebus thought Frollo a cruel and angry man.

Meanwhile, in the cathedral, Quasimodo was talking with his only friends – three gargoyles called Hugo, Victor and Laverne. They were trying to persuade him to go out and join the fun of the festival. Finally he agreed to go, although he knew Frollo would punish him if he found out.

Once outside, Quasimodo panicked – lots of people in fancy dress surrounded him. They were laughing, singing and dancing. Quasimodo had never been close to so many people before. He searched for somewhere to hide and stumbled into Esmeralda's tent.

As soon as he saw the beautiful gypsy girl he moved away, expecting her to make fun of his ugliness. But she just smiled and said, "That's a great mask!"

Esmeralda's compliment made Quasimodo realise that he didn't need a disguise to join the celebrations. Happily, he returned to the square. The crowning of the King of Fools was the highlight of the day and Quasimodo was thrilled when he was chosen.

The crowd thought he was the perfect king. He was given a crown and paraded through the streets. However, the crowd soon began to tease Quasimodo and tied him up. Only Esmeralda came forward to help him.

Enraged at this, Frollo ordered the gypsy girl's arrest. Esmeralda and Djali ran into Notre Dame followed by Phoebus, who had fallen in love with Esmeralda. When Frollo arrived, Phoebus told him that Esmeralda had claimed sanctuary – meaning no harm could come to her inside the cathedral. Frollo left, furious. Phoebus quickly followed him, happy that Esmeralda was safe.

Esmeralda decided to explore the cathedral and spotted Quasimodo hurrying to his room in the tower. She followed him and apologised for what had happened in the square. She told him he was not a monster, but a kind and gentle person. Quasimodo longed to believe her.

After Quasimodo had shown Esmeralda the miniature model of Paris he had built in his room, he offered to help her and Djali escape from the cathedral. Carrying them both in his strong arms, he leapt from the bell tower and climbed down the side of the cathedral. When they reached the ground, Esmeralda gave Quasimodo a woven necklace with a map on it. "It will help you find our Court of Miracles," she said. Then she fled.

When Frollo heard that Esmeralda had escaped he ordered his soldiers to search everywhere, but they found no trace of her. In his rage, Frollo set fire to a miller's home, pretending that the family had sheltered gypsies.

Phoebus, shocked to see how truly evil Frollo was, bravely rescued the miller and his family. Frollo ordered his arrest for disobeying orders. Suddenly, Esmeralda, who had been hiding nearby, frightened Frollo's horse, causing a distraction. Quickly, Phoebus tried to escape. But as he sped away Frollo's soldiers took aim and fired...

An arrow struck Phoebus and he fell, unconscious, into a river. Frollo, thinking he was dead, left him there.

But Phoebus was alive and Esmeralda rescued him and took him back to Notre Dame. There she asked Quasimodo to protect Phoebus from Frollo.

Quasimodo was overjoyed to see Esmeralda again, thinking she had come back because she loved him. However, he quickly realised that she thought of him only as a friend. When he overheard her talking gently to the wounded Phoebus he understood how deep her feelings for the Captain were. Though he tried to hide it, Quasimodo was filled with sadness.

Suddenly, they heard Frollo's carriage outside.
Esmeralda turned to Quasimodo and said, "Promise
me you won't let anything happen to Phoebus." Then
she left. Quasimodo quickly hid Phoebus under a table.

When Frollo walked in, he saw Quasimodo gazing at
his miniature city. Picking up the tiny wooden figure of
Esmeralda, Frollo snarled, "She will torment you no
longer. I know where the gypsies' hideout is.
Tomorrow at dawn I will attack with a thousand men!"

Quasimodo and Phoebus knew they had to warn Esmeralda of Frollo's wicked plans. Following the map on Esmeralda's necklace, they found the Court of Miracles. But once inside, the gypsy leader ordered their capture, believing they were Frollo's spies. Esmeralda burst through the crowd and explained that they had helped her. The gypsies realised she was speaking the truth and listened as Phoebus and Quasimodo warned them about Frollo's attack.

It was too late… Frollo and his soldiers had already arrived. They took Quasimodo, Phoebus, Esmeralda and the other gypsies away. Phoebus was thrown into a cage along with the gypsies and Quasimodo was chained up in the bell tower.

That night, Esmeralda was taken to the town square, where she was tied to a stake. Frollo sentenced her to death. Phoebus watched helplessly from his cage as Frollo walked slowly towards Esmeralda.

Up in the bell tower, Quasimodo struggled to break free from his chains. Gathering all his strength, he pulled and pulled until at last the pillars around him crumbled.

He was free!

Quasimodo quickly swung down from the cathedral and rescued Esmeralda, who had fainted. Then he carried her back up to his bell tower. Standing on the balcony, he held her body high above him for all to see. "Sanctuary!" he cried. "Sanctuary!"

Then, thinking she was dead, Quasimodo gently put Esmeralda on a bed of straw. He thought his heart would break with sorrow. He walked out onto the balcony and saw Frollo gathering his soldiers in the square below. "Seize the cathedral!" Frollo screamed. As Quasimodo looked down at them he was overcome with anger. He couldn't let Frollo win!

Meanwhile, Phoebus had freed himself and the gypsies. Leaping on top of a cage, he called out to the crowd.

"Citizens of Paris," he cried, "Frollo has wronged our people and ransacked our city. Now he has declared war on Notre Dame. Will we allow it?"

"No!" shouted the angry crowd. A fierce battle followed…

Up in the bell tower, Quasimodo and the gargoyles were doing their best to hold off Frollo's men by throwing pieces of wood over the side of the cathedral. Quasimodo didn't know how much longer he could last but the gargoyles encouraged him to carry on. In desperation, he tipped a pot of molten lead over the cathedral's wall. The soldiers scattered but Frollo managed to dodge the shower of lead and enter Notre Dame.

When Frollo reached the bell tower he found
Quasimodo weeping over Esmeralda's body.
"You've killed her!" Quasimodo cried.
"She was my friend."

"*I* am your only friend," Frollo replied. "Let us not
argue, but pray together." However, as
Quasimodo knelt he saw Frollo raise
a dagger to strike him. Quasimodo
managed to throw the dagger aside
then he knocked Frollo to the floor.

Suddenly, Esmeralda woke up.
Quasimodo ran to her side to
lift her to safety. Frollo, his sword
drawn, followed them out onto
the balcony.

After a struggle, Frollo
lost his balance… and fell
to the square below.

Quasimodo lost his balance, too. Esmeralda grabbed his hand, but she couldn't hold on and Quasimodo began to fall. Suddenly, from a ledge below, Phoebus reached out and caught him – Quasimodo was safe!

Next morning, a happy crowd gathered in the square to celebrate their victory over Frollo. As Phoebus and Esmeralda walked out of the cathedral, they were greeted by cheers. A moment later, Quasimodo came out and the crowd became silent.

No one was sure what to say or do until a little girl walked up to Quasimodo. Without a word, she gently touched his face.

The crowd burst into cheers. "Hooray for Quasimodo!" they cried. "Hooray for our hero!"

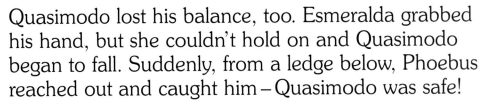

As the crowd lifted him onto their shoulders and paraded him through Paris, Quasimodo thought his heart would burst with happiness. Celebrating with his new friends, he knew that never again would he have to hide, frightened and alone, in the darkness.